KU-575-308

Penguin Book 1997

THE PENGUIN BROCKBANK

Russell Brockbank was born at Niagara Falls, Canada, in 1913 and by 1917 was drawing cars and aeroplanes. He was educated at Ridley College, Ontario, and after coming to England in 1929 attended Chelsea School of Art. In 1932 he was lured into industry but by 1936 had realized – without ever having made any – that money wasn't everything. He then began freelancing and became a contributor to *Punch* after his father bet him he couldn't. Served in the lower deck and as a Lieut. R.N.V.R. on Northern Convoys and in the Pacific. He freelanced until 1949, when he was invited to be Art Editor of *Punch*, from which he resigned in 1960 to draw in peace in Thursley, Surrey, where he lives with his wife and the fastest cars he can afford. He has one son and one daughter. His first book of drawings was *Round the Bend* (1948), followed by *Up the Straight* (1953), *Over the Line* (1955), *The Brockbank Omnibus* (1957), *Manifold Pressures* (1958), and *Move Over* (1962).

The Penguin BROCKBANK

PENGUIN BOOKS

Penguin Books Ltd, Harmondsworth, Middlesex
U.S.A.: Penguin Books Inc., 3300 Clipper Mill Road, Baltimore 11, Md
AUSTRALIA: Penguin Books Pty Ltd, 762 Whitehorse Road, Mitcham, Victoria

This selection published in Penguin Books 1963

This selection copyright © Penguin Books Ltd, 1963

*The drawings on the title page and pp. 5–65, 77, 80, 82, 96, 106–8, 111
(bottom), 113 (bottom), 114–15, 118, and 126–7 are copyright and are
reproduced by kind permission of* Punch. *The remaining drawings are
copyright to the Motor and are reproduced by kind permission of the
Temple Press from* Up the Straight *and* Over the Line

Made and printed in Great Britain
by Hazells Offset Ltd, Slough, Bucks
Set in Monotype Romulus

This book is sold subject to the condition that it shall not, by
way of trade, be lent, re-sold, hired out, or otherwise disposed of without
the publisher's consent, in any form of binding or cover
other than that in which it is published

BEWARE
SUDDEN
AIRCRAFT
NOISES

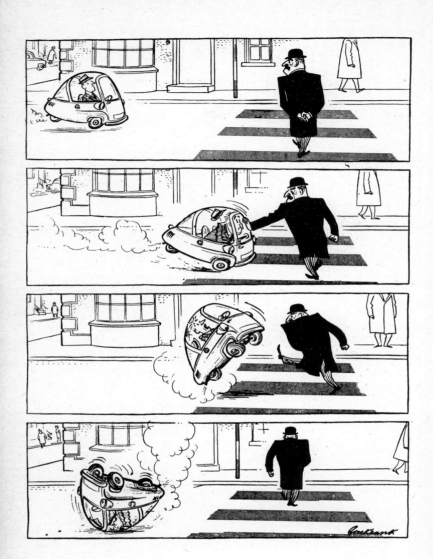

'*Straight on be quicker, but t'other be prettier.*'

'I should have thought there was enough crime in the newspapers without having it in real life, too.'

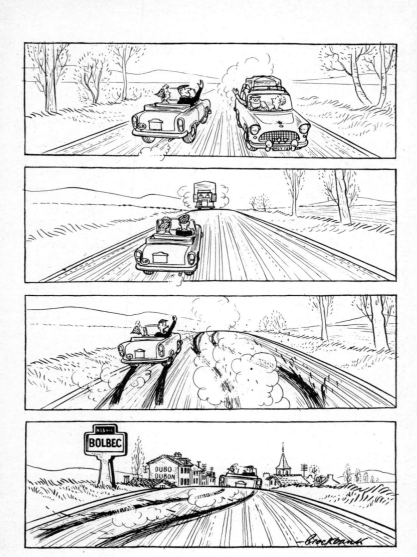

'While you're about it, ask him if he knows a good place for lunch.'

'Why, Mr Moskvitch, I thought we said good-bye to you
at the Polish frontier.'

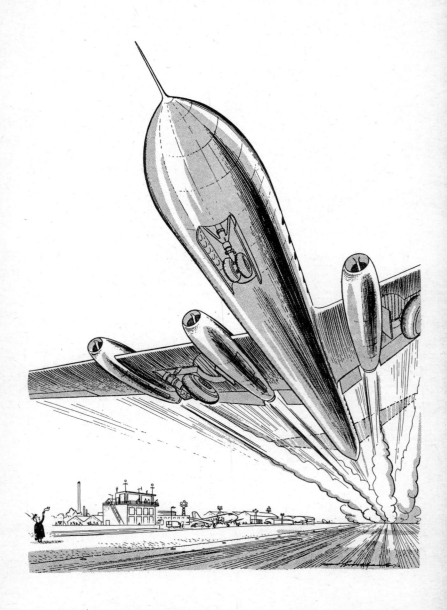

'I told you something awful would happen.'

'. . . and there is a gentleman from the Dingbat Aero Company
waiting outside.'

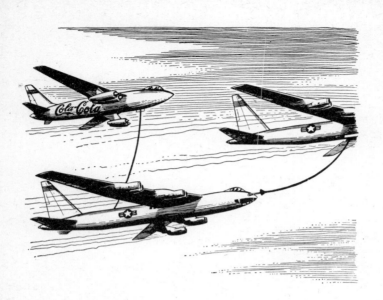

'Get a load of the air hostess.'

'Time of arrival 14 hours, 37 minutes, 7 secs. . . . 8 secs. . . . 9 secs. . . .'

'Ah, shut up!'

'They're accurate to a thou., so there's no need to keep saying
"And the best of luck." '

' – and we finally designed the most scientifically functional chair it
was possible to conceive; and this, I am sorry to say, is it.'

'Originally it was on TV'

'It's been done!'

'*I name this ship* Veuve Cliquot 1937. . . .'

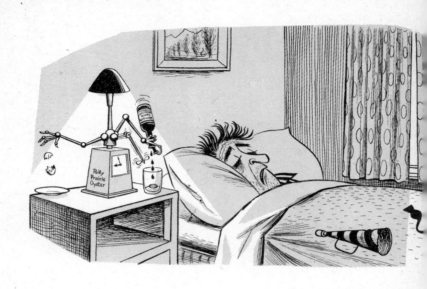

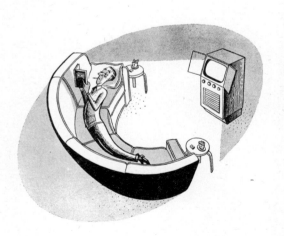

'If business doesn't improve, we shall have to take larger premises.'

'I do hope these new neighbours aren't going to be noisy.'

(1)

(2)

(3)

(4)

(5)

(6)

(7)

'Game, Set, Match – Net!'

'Now let's take the hypothetical case of a person not wanting to go by way of the old stile, *Seven Acre Meadow*, and *Bluebell Wood*. . . .'

'Driving without lights, impersonating an officer, and sounding your horn after 11 p.m. in a built-up area.'

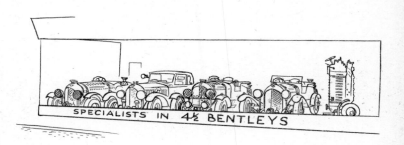

SPECIALISTS IN 4½ BENTLEYS

'I call it jolly neighbourly of you, Mr Fosdyke, to give me the benefit of your thirty years' experience on the road. . . .'

'Now, gentlemen, I respect your feelings, but one of you
must *have* been driving.'

'My father's a racing driver.'

'It was 7.30 for 8, surely?'

'*Please can we have our ball race back?*'

'– In case you didn't know, it's easier to swing the camera.'

'. . . *return you to the studio.*'

'Hullo, Mum and Dad and all at home!'

'All I can hear is a high-pitched scream rising in pitch.'

'Oh, well – nothing venture,
nothing win.'

CITRON PRESSÉ

'Now is that a tappet, or isn't it?'

'*But how cosy!* I'm *insured with you!*'

'I warned him this was no country for eight-horsepower cars.'

'Back a bit . . .

. . . bit more . . .

. . . more . . .

. . . more . . .

~~~ C-U-R-U-N-C-H ~~~

'Whoa.'

'Just what kind of a drive in the country had you in mind?'

'*By Gad, there are moments when I regret I ever joined.*'

'*Streamline? Streamline? What do you want with streamline?*'

'We like it here so much we haven't bothered to go any further.'

'That's nothing like the "Turning Left" signal you taught me.'

' . . . To whom it may concern, I am about to put
on my brakes, hard.'

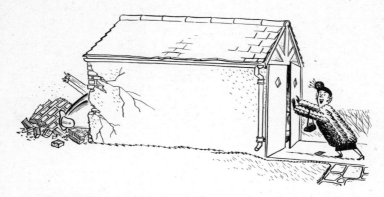

'Who said you couldn't back the new car in – and close the doors!'

'One thing about a breakdown – it gives you a chance
to look at the scenery.'

'I've had enough of your thinly veiled insults.'

'He's either an absolute outsider or a famous racing driver.'

'If anything, we're getting more power than we know
what to do with.'

'By God, Emily – we've got the Death Watch Beetle
in the station wagon now.'

'Damn these opening windscreens.'

'Flyovers, Motorways, and such! What's the matter
with the roads we've got?'

PENGUIN HUMOUR

The following books of cartoons and humour are being
published in Penguins simultaneously:

THE PENGUIN THELWELL · 2006

U.S.A. FOR BEGINNERS · 2022
Alex Atkinson and Ronald Searle

THE PENGUIN HOFFNUNG · 2039

THE JENGUIN PENNINGS · 2051*
Paul Jennings

Also available:

THE BIG CITY · 1856
Alex Atkinson and Ronald Searle

THE PENGUIN CHARLES ADDAMS · 1845**

THE PENGUIN MAX · 1825**
Giovannetti

THE LOVERS · 1660
Raymond Peynet

* NOT FOR SALE IN THE U.S.A.
** NOT FOR SALE IN THE U.S.A. OR CANADA

*For a complete list of books available please write to Penguin Books
whose address can be found on the back of the title page*